Elementary Grade Four

The Wisdom of Our Prophet ﷺ

Workbook

Dr. Tasneema Ghazi
Rahayu Mohamad

 IQRA' International Educational Foundation

Part of a Comprehensive and Systematic Program of Islamic Studies

A workbook of the program of *Sirah* and *Hadith* Elementary Level Grade - 4

The Wisdom of Our Prophet ﷺ

Chief Program Editors

Dr. Abidullah Ghazi
(Ph.D., Study of Religion
Harvard University)

Dr. Tasneema Ghazi
(Ph.D., Curriculum-Reading
University of Minnesota)

Editing

Nilofer Ali-Rodgers
Samana Khan

Design

Aliuddin Khaja

Production Manager

Aliuddin Khaja

First Edition, May 2011
Printed in USA

Copyright © 2011, IQRA' International Educational Foundation.
All Rights Reserved

ISBN # 1-56316-189-3

IQRA' Note

Our purpose in producing these workbooks is to provide students with a tool for reinforcement of the material covered in the corresponding textbook. Both the Wisdom of Our Prophet textbook and workbook have been designed to instill love for the Messenger of Allah ﷺ and devotion to his teachings in the student.

The exercises provided in this workbook are developed with an understanding of the abilities and interests of nine and ten year olds. It is our hope that students will be able to grasp the concepts introduced by each lesson; in so much as they will gain the literal and inferential comprehension of the textbook's lessons.

IQRA' workbooks are an integral part of our professionally-designed program of Islamic education. We recommend that teachers use these workbooks in conjunction with their companion textbooks as the school year progresses. All IQRA' workbooks are designed to provide students with important exercises in comprehension and critical thinking skills.

We invite you to join hands with us in our efforts by sending us your valuable comments and suggestions. Let's all begin to build to place the building blocks of spiritual and moral development in our children, so that they may be able to take on the challenges of the world around them with firm Iman and Taqwa. We continually seek Allah's forgiveness and support and ask that He forever sends peace and blessings upon the Crown of Creation, Sayyidina Muhammad Mustafa ﷺ!

Chief Editors

May, 2011
Jumada al-Thani, 1432

Table of Contents

Table of Contents

THE QUR'AN AND HADITH

Activity 1: Comprehension

What are the two things Rasulullah ﷺ asked us to "hold on to?"

The two things Rasulullah asked us to hold on to are Allah's book and the sunnah

Why did he ask us to hold on to these?

He asked us to hold on to these because they will make our life successful and astray.

Activity 2 – Think About It!

Qur'an

Write two ways in which the Qur'an and Hadith are alike.

Hadith

1. They have never been changed for 1,400 years.

2. They are Islam

Qur'an

Write two ways in which the Qur'an and Hadith are different.

Hadith

Qur'an box:
Quran is the words of Allah. Arabic. Classical

Hadith box:
Hadith is the words of Rusulullah. Detailed.

Activity 3: Writing a Paragraph

Write a paragraph about the miracle of the Qur'an. Use the sentence-starters below to write your paragraphs:

Topic Sentence: The Qur'an is a miracle.

Reason 1: **Because,** it has never been changed for 1,400 year

Reason 2: **Also,** it was revealed at the specil night of Ramadan.

Closing sentence - **I think** I will finish the Quran. (inshallah)

Now write your paragraph. Don't forget to indent the first line!

The Hadith is a miracale because peopel went careful with it , why?→ if they change some of it prophet Muhammad will go into Hell.

Activity 4 - Vocabulary

Complete following crossword puzzle.

1 (across): U m m a h
2 (down): r a h m a n
3 (across): A r R a h e e m
4 (across): Q u r a n
5 (down): h a d i t
7 (across): _ _ a _ _ _ _
8 (down): G r a c i o u s
9 (across): _ _ _ _ _ _
10 (across): S a h a b a h
11 (down): S u n n a h

Directions

Across

1. The worldwide Muslim community
3. Attribute of Allah ﷻ given in Surah Al-Fatihah (Arabic)
4. The words of Allah ﷻ sent to Rasulullah ﷺ
7. A level of excellence to be met
9. People born and living at about the same time
10. The companions of Rasulullah ﷺ

Down

2. Attribute of Allah ﷻ given in Surah Al-Fatihah (Arabic)
5. Written record of the Sunnah
6. Meaning of Ar-Rahim, mentioned in Surah Al-Fatihah
8. Meaning of Ar-Rahman, mentioned in Surah Al-Fatihah
10. All the actions, sayings and practices of Rasulullah ﷺ

UNDERSTANDING THE HADITH

Activity 1: Comprehension

Name the three parts of a Hadith, and explain why each is important:

1. _Isnad_ is important because _it tells us the chain the narrators of the Hadith_

2. _Matn._ is important because _it's the actual text of the Hadith._ ← it tells the main part of the had it

3. _Hadith colletion_ is important because _it is how the Hadith was found._

Activity 2 – Think About It!

Write some of the ways people collected Ahadith in the past. Imagine you are collecting Ahadith today. Explain how you would do each of the tasks below.

Task	Ways used in the past	Ways that can be used today
Recording Ahadith		
Comparing Ahadith		
Listing reporters		
Check honesty		

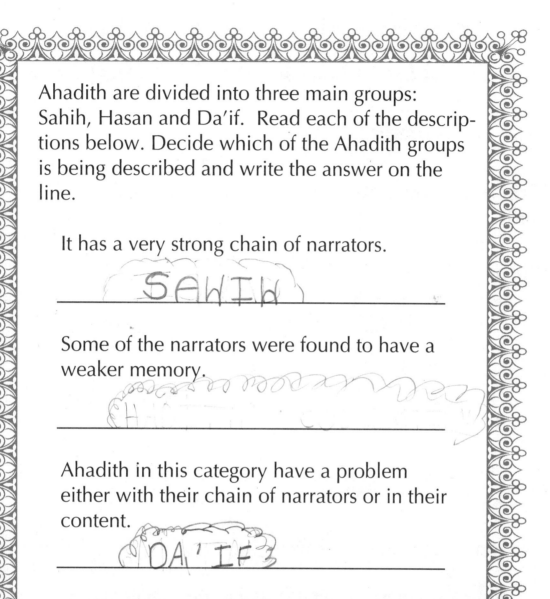

Ahadith are divided into three main groups: Sahih, Hasan and Da'if. Read each of the descriptions below. Decide which of the Ahadith groups is being described and write the answer on the line.

It has a very strong chain of narrators.

_____SAHIH_____

Some of the narrators were found to have a weaker memory.

_____H_____

Ahadith in this category have a problem either with their chain of narrators or in their content.

_____DA'IF_____

3

THE MAJOR COMPILERS OF AHADITH AND THEIR BOOKS

Activity 1: Comprehension

Directions: Read the following sentences and fill in the missing words.

Words:

memorized	Ahadith	generation	write

a. The Sahabah received ___Ahadith___ directly from Rasulullah ﷺ.

b. The Sahabah ___memorized___ the words of guidance spoken by Rasulullah ﷺ.

c. Some Sahabah were able to ___write___ down Ahadith.

d. After Rasulullah ﷺ left this world, the Sahabah passed the knowledge of the Ahadith to the next ___generation___.

Activity 2: Critical Thinking

Directions: Finish the sentences below about the six Sahih Ahadith collections.

Name the Book(s) of Ahadith
a. that are included in the six Sahih Ahadith collections:

سنن أبي داود   سنن النسائي   صحيح مسلم   صحيح البخاري

سنن ابن ماجة   سنن الترمذي

b. whose compilers were from Iran: <u>Sahih muslim, Sunan Abu Dawud, Sunan at-Tirmidhi, Sunan an-Nasai</u>

c. whose compilers began the study of Ahadith at the ages of 9 and 15: <u>Sunan an-Nasai, Imam al-Bukhari</u>

d. compiled by Imam al-Bukhari: <u>Sahih al-Bukhari</u>

e. which includes 4,314 Sahih Ahadith: <u>Sunan ibn Majah</u>

Activity 3: Geo Link

Directions: Look at the map of Asia below. Color the countries where the six famous compilers of Ahadith were born.

4

SEEKING KNOWLEDGE

Activity 1

Directions: Write a short story about a day you spent in school learning with your teachers and friends.

Remember in this lesson's Hadith that you are "In the way of Allah" from the time you leave for school until you return home. Make your story personal. You need to be creative and have fun!

Use the following cards to take notes before you write your story.

I _____
_____
_____
_____
_____

I got on _____
_____
_____ I got off _____
_____
_____ I went in _____

And then _____
_____
_____
_____
I played _____

I saw _____
_____
I asked _____
_____

I learned _____
_____
_____
_____
_____

I ate _____
_____
_____
I played _____
_____

Then, it was time to _____
_____
_____
_____
_____

Now write your story!

_____
_____
_____
_____
_____
_____
_____
_____
_____
_____
_____
_____
_____
_____
_____
_____
_____
_____
_____
_____
_____
_____
_____

Activity 3: Making Connections

Directions: Read about early schools and universities set up by Muslims. Answer the questions which follow.

Al-Azhar University

Al-Azhar University was built around 970 CE by the Fatimid rulers of Egypt. The university can be found in the famous city of Cairo. Because the Fatimid rulers were the great-grandchildren of Rasulullah's daughter Fatimah az-Zahra, they named the university in her honor. Al-Azhar is believed to be the second oldest university in the world!

Originally only Islamic law, Arabic, philosophy and astronomy were taught in al-Azhar. But in 1961 the school started having classes in science, medicine, economics, agriculture and engineering.

Al-Azhar as produced many great Islamic scholars. These scholars had a big influence on the lives of countless people.

University of Al-Qarawiyyin

Al-Qarawayyin was founded in 859 in the city of Fez, Moraco by a noble lady named Fatima al-Fihri. At first this schools was a part of a mosque. However, it soon grew into a place of religious learning. Slowly but surely the subjects offered at Al-Qarawayyin included mathematics, languages, medicine, chemistry, history, geography and music.

During the Middle Ages Jewish, Christian and Muslim scolars studied at Al-Qarawayyin. The university played a leading role in cultural exchange and the transfer of knowledge between the Muslim and Christian worlds. Famous scholars such as Ibn al-Arabi (1165-1240 AD), Ibn Khaldun (1332-1395 AD), Leo Africanus , Rabbi Maimonides and many more were connected with Al-Qarawayyin either as students or lecturers.

This university is considered by the Guinness Book of World Records as the oldest continuously operating university in the world. The university has been (and still is) one of the leading spiritual and educational centers of the Muslim world.

Questions:

How is Al-Qarawiyyin a Sadaqah Jariyah (continuous charity) for the noble lady Fatima al-Fihri?

_____

_____

_____

_____

Activity 3 – Think About It!

Read the paragraphs about Al-Qarawiyyin and Al-Azhar University. How did North Africa help the spread of knowledge around the world? Write a few sentences.

_____

_____

_____

_____

_____

_____

_____

How are these two schools following the Hadith of Prophet Muhammad ?

_____

_____

_____

_____

_____

_____

_____

5

THE STATUS OF THE PEOPLE OF KNOWLEDGE

Activity 1: Comprehension

Prophet Muhammad ﷺ said that people with knowledge are like the "full moon among the stars." Those who just obey and worship Allah ﷻ are like stars. Circle the correct answer to each question.

A. The Moon's bright light is actually a reflection of the Sun's light. Whose light do the learned scholars of Islam reflect?

☑ Rasulullah ﷺ   ☐ Books   ☐ The internet

B. Whose high rank does this lesson's Hadith talk about?

☐ A pious lady   ☑ Learned scholars   ☐ The president

C. What did Imam al-Bukhari leave us?

☐ A beautiful palace   ☐ Gold and silver   ☑ Useful knowledge

D. What is the responsibility of the scholars of Islam?

☐ To sit and relax   ☑ To learn and teach

☐ To boss people around

Activity 2 - Show What You Know

Read the following statements found in this lesson's Hadith. Then pick one statement and represent it using a form of art (for example make a drawing, a poster, or a collage).

Statements:

1. "The inhabitants of the heaven and earth"
2. "The fish in the depth of the sea"
3. "The superiority of a learned person over an obedient worshipper is like that of a full moon to the rest of the stars."

Share your beautiful work and display it in your classroom.

Activity 3 – Puzzle Time

Help Imran find his way to the Masjid.

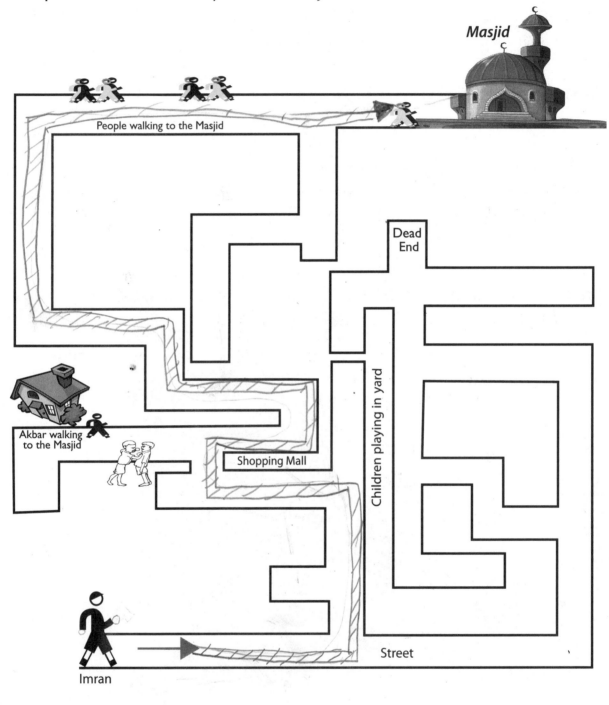

Masjid

People walking to the Masjid

Dead End

Akbar walking to the Masjid

Children playing in yard

Shopping Mall

Street

Imran

6

WHO IS THE MUTTAQI?

Activity 1: Comprehension

"Have Taqwa wherever you are, and follow a bad deed with a good one, because this will erase it. Also, deal with people using good manners." (Sunan at-Tirmidhi)

Question

What are the three main teachings of this lesson's Hadith?

i. _____
_____
_____

ii. _____
_____
_____

iii _____
_____
_____

Activity 2: Critical Thinking

Below is a list of the characteristics of a Muttaqi. Match the characteristics to the following events:

The characteristics of a Muttaqi:

- Feeling the presence of Allah ﷻ
- Complete trust in Allah ﷻ
- Asking for Allah's forgiveness after making a mistake

A. An army of 313 Muslims defeated an army of 1,000 Kuffar at the Battle of Badr.

_____

_____

_____

B. Hatib ؓ secretly tried to inform the Kuffar about the Muslims' plans to take Makkah. He realized his mistake and asked for forgiveness from Allah ﷻ and Rasulullah ﷺ.

_____

_____

_____

C. Hajar ؓ stayed in the desert valley with her baby Isma'il and felt that Allah ﷻ was always with her and her baby.

_____

_____

_____

Activity 3

A. In each bubble below write an adjective that describes a Muttaqi. A Muttaqi is a person who has excellent manners and behavior.

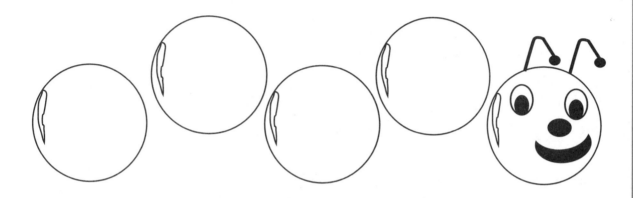

B. Next, choose two words from above and write a sentence about each.

1. _____

   _____

2. _____

   _____

7

THE SPIRIT OF IHSAN

Activity 1: Comprehension

Read the statement and answer the question:

"Ihsan is to worship Allah as if you see Him. It is realizing that even if you cannot see Him, He is always seeing you."

A. Hina found a fancy pen on her way to school. She took it to the lost and found at school so that it can get to the person who lost it.

Does Hina's action show Ihsan?

 Yes No

Explain.
Because Hina didn't steal and she knew that Allah is watching her.

B. Sulaiman tells his parents that he is going to the library so he can study.
Instead, he goes to his friend's house to play video games.

Does Sulaiman's action show Ihsan?

Explain.

Because he lied to his parents.

Activity 2 - Think About It

Read the story of Prophet Yusuf ﷺ at the end of this lesson. Write down at least three of his actions that showed Ihsan in the space below.

1. He didn't take revenge

2. He brang his family together

3.

Activity 3 - Vocabulary

Find each of the following words.

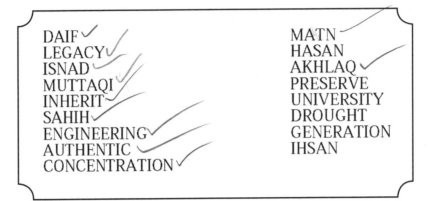

DAIF
LEGACY
ISNAD
MUTTAQI
INHERIT
SAHIH
ENGINEERING
AUTHENTIC
CONCENTRATION

MATN
HASAN
AKHLAQ
PRESERVE
UNIVERSITY
DROUGHT
GENERATION
IHSAN

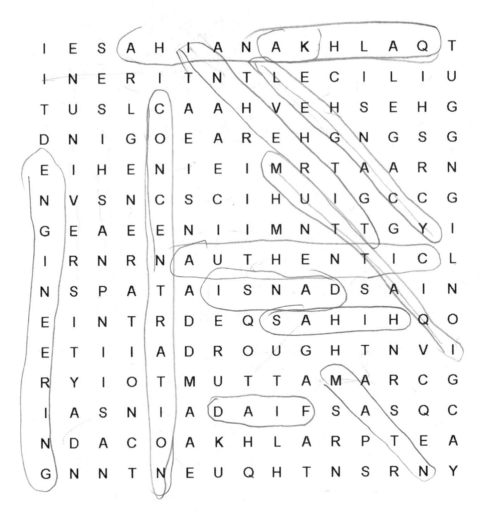

```
I  E  S  A  H  I  A  N  A  K  H  L  A  Q  T
I  N  E  R  I  T  N  T  L  E  C  I  L  I  U
T  U  S  L  C  A  A  H  V  E  H  S  E  H  G
D  N  I  G  O  E  A  R  E  H  G  N  G  S  G
E  I  H  E  N  I  E  I  M  R  T  A  A  R  N
N  V  S  N  C  S  C  I  H  U  I  G  C  C  G
G  E  A  E  E  N  I  I  M  N  T  T  G  Y  I
I  R  N  R  N  A  U  T  H  E  N  T  I  C  L
N  S  P  A  T  A  I  S  N  A  D  S  A  I  N
E  I  N  T  R  D  E  Q  S  A  H  I  H  Q  O
E  T  I  I  A  D  R  O  U  G  H  T  N  V  I
R  Y  I  O  T  M  U  T  T  A  M  A  R  C  G
I  A  S  N  I  A  D  A  I  F  S  A  S  Q  C
N  D  A  C  O  A  K  H  L  A  R  P  T  E  A
G  N  N  T  N  E  U  Q  H  T  N  S  R  N  Y
```

8

ALLAH'S FORGIVENESS AND MERCY

Activity 1: Comprehension

Put the steps of asking for forgiveness in order by numbering the sentences below:

_2_ Have complete trust in Allah ﷻ

_3_ Ask Allah ﷻ sincerely for forgiveness

_1_ Recognize that you made a mistake.

_4_ Decide to never make the same mistake again

Activity 2 - Allah's Attributes

Read the following attributes of Allah ﷻ in English. Then match the Arabic word to its correct English meaning.

Arabic	English
العفو	The Generous One
الكريم	The One who Pardons
الرحيم	The Loving
الودود	The Merciful
الغفار	The One Who gives forgiveness
الرحمن	The Beneficent

Use at least two of Allah's special names from the previous page to explain why we should ask for Allah's forgiveness when we make a mistake.

_____

_____

Activity 3 - Think About It

Rasulullah ﷺ forgave Hatib ؓ completely and never reminded him of his mistake. Rasulullah ﷺ never mentioned what Hatib ؓ did to other people. He covered up Hatib's mistake.

Allah ﷻ wants us to forgive others just as He forgives us. So let us make the following four promises when someone has offended or hurt us!

*To:*_____

*From:*_____

1. *I promise that I will think good thoughts about you, Insha Allah.*
2. *I promise that I will not bring up this situation to use against you.*
3. *I promise that I will not talk to others about what you did.*
4. *I promise that I will forgive you with all sincerity and honesty.*

*Signed:*_____

*Date:*_____

Activity 4 - Use What You Know

We make mistakes many times. However, Allah ﷻ is Most Merciful. Whenever we seek His forgiveness, He forgives us.

Write a special Du'a asking Allah ﷻ to forgive one or more mistakes you have made.

Bismillah Ar Rahman Ar Rahim

_____

_____

_____

_____

_____

_____

_____

_____

_____

_____

_____

9

FOLLOWING THE PROPHET ﷺ

Activity 1: Comprehension

Use the telegraph codes in the rectangle below to decode Allah's commands about following Rasulullah ﷺ.

A ●—	N —●
B —●●●	O ———
C —●—●	P ●——●
D —●●	Q ——●—
E ●	R ●—●
F ●●—●	S ●●●
G ——●	T —
H ●●●●	U ●●—
I ●●	V ●●●—
J ●———	X —●●—
K —●—	Y —●——
L ●—●●	W ●——
M ——	Z ——●●

YOU SHOULD

ACCEPT

WHATEVER

THE

MESSENGER

GIVES YOU

Decode the Ayah

You should accept whatever the Messenger Gives you.

_____

Explain what you learned from this Ayah and from the lesson you just read:

I learned you should believe in each other and accept whatever the Messenger says.

Activity 2

We are going to follow Rasulullah ﷺ by making someone feel special. We'll try to bring a smile to his or her face, Inshallah.

Learn how to make a gift basket on the next page. Then attach the card below to your basket.

> *I just wanted to make you feel special today.*
> *This is a little gift from* __Eesha)__

Give your gift to someone who does not live with you at home. This can be a neighbor, friend, or classmate.

(From: http://tlc.howstuffworks.com/family/paper-baskets1.htm)

African Tutsi Basket

Make an African Tutsi Basket that resembles the grass baskets used by the Tutsi people of Africa.

The Tutsi people make these baskets by coiling long strands of dried grass around and around. Bind them together with thinner strands. The baskets have lids and are used to hold grain. Hold your own treasures in your own basket!

What you'll need:

- 2 sheets 9x12-inch red construction paper
- 3 sheets 9x12-inch beige construction paper
- 5-inch plate
- 9-inch plate

Tools:

- Clear tape
- Ruler
- Pencil
- Scissors
- Craft glue

Step 1: Cut 8 strips of red construction paper. Each strip should be 12 inches long and 3/4 inch wide. With 2 pieces of the beige construction paper, glue the 12-inch-long edges of the pieces together (overlap the edges a little). After the glue has dried, cut 4 strips 16 inches long and 1/2 inch wide.

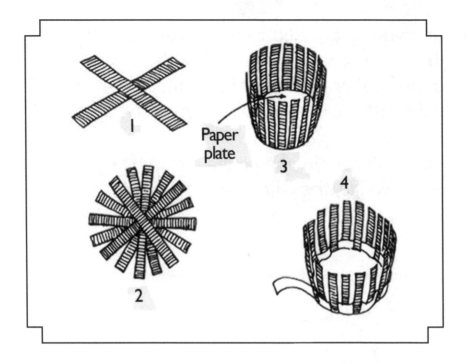

Follow these steps to create the
African Tutsi Paper Basket.

Step 2: Glue 2 red strips together at the middle to form a cross. Do this with all the other red strips until you have 4 red crosses. Place the 4 crosses on top of each other, and fan them out evenly. Glue them in place -- they should look like a star.

Step 3: Use the 5-inch plate to draw a circle on the other piece of red construction paper. Cut out the circle, and glue it to the center of the star. This forms the bottom of your basket. Fold the rays of the star up at the edge of the circle.

Step 4: Tape a beige strip horizontally across the bottom of 1 ray. Weave the beige strip over and under the rays all the way around. Remove the tape, and glue the ends of the beige strip together. Hold ends together until glue begins to dry. Repeat with remaining beige strips. Push beige strips close together before gluing.

Step 5: After you›ve finished weaving the beige strips, fold over and glue the red ends to the inside of the basket, forming a rim. Make a pointed lid for the basket by using the 9-inch plate to trace a circle on the last sheet of beige construction paper.

Step 6: Cut out the circle, then cut a pie wedge out of the circle (the bigger the wedge, the taller the lid). Overlap and glue the cut ends together.

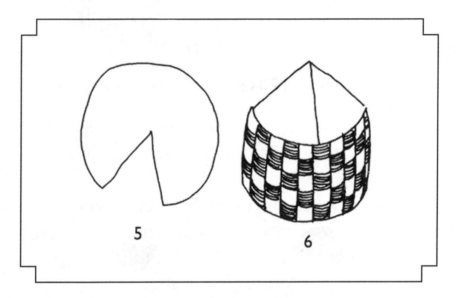

Make the lid of the African Tutsi Paper Basket.

Now you've got your very own African Tutsi paper basket -- what will you put inside? Note: If you don't want to use red and beige paper, use any 2 colors you'd like.

Tall People, Small Baskets
Baskets made by the Tutsi people of central Africa may be small, but the Tutsi people are among the tallest in the world. In fact, the Tutsi are often more than 7 feet in height. The Tutsi live in round grass huts scattered throughout the hilly countryside.

Activity 3 – Geography Connection: The Isra and Miraj

Look at the map of the Middle East and—

A. Locate the city of Makkah
B. Locate the city of Jerusalem
C. Label the three bodies of water that touch the Arabian Penninsula.

IBADAH: THE WAY OF A BELIEVER

Activity 1: Comprehension

Read this lesson's Hadith:

"Worship the Most Compassionate, feed the needy, spread peace and you will enter Paradise calmly." (Sunan at-Tirmidhi)

Look at the pictures below and color those which will get us to Jannah. Under each picture, write the part of the Hadith that it shows someone performing.

Activity 2 - Think about it

Circle the examples below that describe proper 'Ibadah. On the line next to each, explain why it is or is not an example of proper 'Ibadah.

- (•) Help victims of an earthquake. _Helping the needy_
- (•) Perform Salah five times each day. _Worshipping Allah_
- ✗ Eat delicious steamed vegetables. _____
- ✗ Go to a movie with friends. _____
- (•) Give your pocket money to a charity. _Zakat_
- ✗ Argue with your elders. _____
- (•) Avoid backbiting. _Ibadah_

Activity 3 - Try to be like the Prophet ﷺ

Think and write what will you do i the following situations:

A. Some of your friends do not want a new student to join your soccer team.

I would convince my team to let the new person in our team.

B. Ahmad, who always makes fun of you and bullies you needs someone to help him in his math homework. You are very good in math.

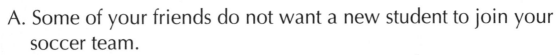

If would make a deal with him, I would say "If you stop bullieing me I will help you with your math homework."

C. Your older neighbor needs some one to help her with the shopping.

I would ask her if she needs help, then I would help her bring the groceries to her house.

Activity 4 - Show What You Know

Let's read this verse of the Qur'an:

لَا تَعْبُدُونَ إِلَّا ٱللَّهَ وَبِٱلْوَٰلِدَيْنِ إِحْسَانًا وَذِى ٱلْقُرْبَىٰ وَٱلْيَتَٰمَىٰ وَٱلْمَسَٰكِينِ وَقُولُوا۟ لِلنَّاسِ حُسْنًا وَأَقِيمُوا۟ ٱلصَّلَوٰةَ وَءَاتُوا۟ ٱلزَّكَوٰةَ ثُمَّ تَوَلَّيْتُمْ إِلَّا قَلِيلًا مِّنكُمْ وَأَنتُم مُّعْرِضُونَ

Worship none but Allah; and to parents be good and to relatives, orphans, and the needy. And speak to people good (words) and establish prayer and give zakah.
(Surah al-Baqarah 2:83)

Read the above verse (2:83) and then read this lesson's Hadith. In the table below write each action Allah ﷻ and Rasulullah ﷺ have asked us to do.

Example: First one is done for you

The Qur'an	The Hadith
1. "Worship none but Allah."	1. "Worship the Most Compassionate."
2. Be good to your parents	2. Feed the needy
3. Give zakah	3. Spread peace
4. Establish pryer	4. Enter paradise calmly

TAHARAH

Activity 1: Comprehension

Work in groups of four to come up with thoughts relating to Taharah.

Use the mind map below as an example. Create your own as a group or use the one below.

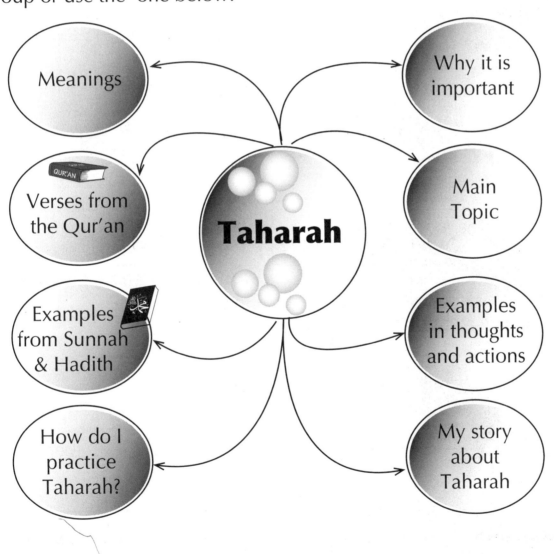

Meanings

Why it is important

Verses from the Qur'an

QUR'AN

Taharah

Main Topic

Examples from Sunnah & Hadith

Examples in thoughts and actions

How do I practice Taharah?

My story about Taharah

Activity 2 - Think About It

Draw a line from the picture on the left to the matching actions on the right explain how we can perform Taharah.

pure thoughts

Ghusl /Wudu

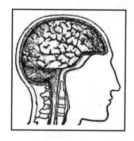

pure feelings

brush, broom, paper towels, cleaning soap etc.

good and polite words, Dhikrullah, reciting the Quran.

Activity 3 - Vocabulary: Homophones

Homophones are words that sound the same but have different meanings. Sometimes homophones are spelled the same, like "rose" (flower) and "rose" (past tense of "rise"). Sometimes they are spelled differently, like "to" and "two."

Use the correct homophone to complete each sentence.

A. Ahmad always _____ Fajr Salah on time.

                prays   preys

B. Saudi Arabia has a large, hot _____.

                desert   dessert

C. 'Isa ﷺ was a _____of Allah ﷻ.

                profit   prophet

D. Scholars are the _____ of the prophets.

                air   heir

E. We ask Allah ﷻ to guide us to the _____ path.

                straight   strait

PRAYING ON TIME

Activity 1: Think About It!

Rasulullah's daily schedule was centered on his Salah. Read his daily schedule below and in the next column write your daily schedule. See if your schedule is also centered around your five daily prayers.

Salah Timing	Rasulullah's Schedule	My Daily Schedule
Fajr	• Before Fajr he got up made Wudu', and prayed in the Masjid. • Spent some time meeting and teaching the people in the Masjid. • After sunrise he would make Ishraq prayer. • Then he would go home and help with the house work. • Sometimes he would meet special visitors.	
Zuhr	• At noon he would go to the Masjid and lead Zuhr prayer. • Then he would go to the bazaar and make sure the merchants were treating people honestly. • He would return home, have lunch and take a short nap called Qailulah.	

Salah Timing	Rasulullah's Schedule	My Daily Schedule
Asr	• At the time of 'Asr prayer he would return to the Masjid and lead the prayer. • After this he would go and visit his wives.	
Maghrib	• He returned to the Masjid for Maghrib prayer. • After prayer, he would go home and teach women about Islam. • He would also answer their questions.	
'Isha	• He would eat his dinner. Then he'd go to the Masjid for 'Isha prayer. • After prayer, he would make Wudu', brush his teeth and get ready to go to bed.	
Tahajjud	• He would wake up in the middle of the night, make Wudu', and do Tahajjud prayer. • He would sleep a little and then wake up again for Fajr.	

Activity 2 - Interview

Interview one of your classmates about his or her daily activities. Write out your interview as a story. Be creative!

Use the following questions to help you with your interview.

1. What is your name?
2. How old are you?
3. How many brothers and sisters do you have?
4. What time do you wake up in the morning?
5. What do you do before leaving for school?
6. What are some things you like about school?
7. Where do you pray Zuhr?
8. What time do you get home from school?
9. Where do you pray 'Asr?
10. What do you do between 'Asr and Maghrib?
11. What sorts of games do you play at home?
12. What is your favorite book?
13. What chores do you do around the house?
14. Does your family pray Maghrib in Jama'ah?
15. Do you finish your homework before or after Maghrib?
16. What time do you make 'Isha prayer?
17. What time do you go to bed?

Write the answers to these questions in your notebook. Then write your story. You may ask more questions if you like.

Activity 3 - Understand and retell

DIRECTIONS

Step 1: Read the story of the Ice seller
Step 2: Fill out the Chart
Step 3: Try to Retell the Story to a friend in your class.

Questions (Things about the story I didn't understand)	Main Points of the Story	This reminds me of	The lesson learned from the Story
I didn't understand when they use to go to mountains and collect ice, ~~ant~~ snow in a container.	• To remember Allah • Use time wisely	it reminds me of Pakistan when they tryed to keep cold water cold. (In shops) Or when people have to go to somewhere far to collect water for there family.	Be on time for Salah and use time wisely.

Activity 4 - Vocabulary

Work with a another student to complete the vocabulary chart below. Choose two vocabulary words from the chart. Use a dictionary to find your answers. Your friend will choose the other two vocabulary words and do the same. Then share your answers with each other.

The first one is done for you.

Vocabulary Word	Definition	Antonym	Synonym	Use in a sentence
Punctual	Being on time	late	prompt	Riza is punctual in offering his salah.
Manage				
Parable				
Pure				
Harmony				

13

THE IMPORTANCE OF FASTING

Activity 1: Comprehension

Read the first paragraph of the "READ AND THINK" section of Lesson 13 in your textbook. Use the ovals to write the three special features of a Hadith Qudsi

....

Hadith Qudsi

....

49

Activity 2 - Think About It!

Create your own graphic organizer like the one below. Use it to write the ways fasting is similar to other acts of 'Ibadah (Salah, Zakah, or Hajj) and the ways it's different.

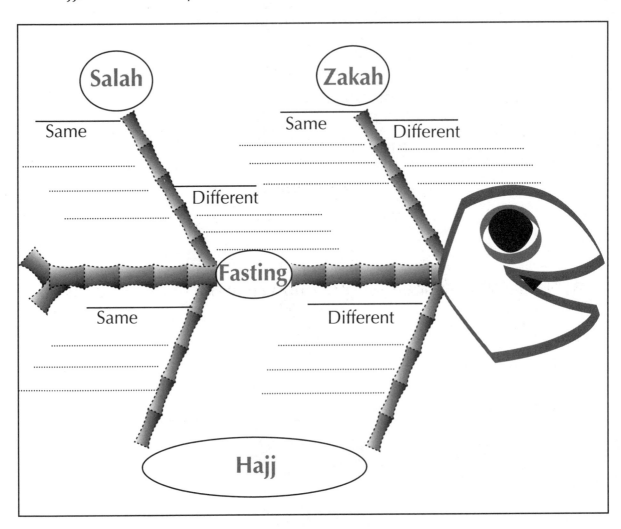

Areas to compare:

Action (what is the action we do?) _____

Benefit to us (how do we benefit?) _____

Frequency (how often do we do it?) _____

Activity 3 - Show What You Know

Read the following verse of the Qur'an and answer the questions which follow.

يَـٰٓأَيُّهَا ٱلَّذِينَ ءَامَنُواْ كُتِبَ عَلَيْكُمُ ٱلصِّيَامُ كَمَا كُتِبَ عَلَى ٱلَّذِينَ مِن قَبْلِكُمْ لَعَلَّكُمْ تَتَّقُونَ ﴿١٨٣﴾

O you who Believe! The fasting is prescribed to you as it was prescribed to those before you in order for you become Muttaqi.
(Surah al-Baqara 2:183)

A. Name two prophets whose followers were required to fast:

1. _____

2. _____

51

14

CHARITY AND GENEROSITY

Activity 1: Comprehension

Read the Hadith on page 54 of your textbook. Write act of charity illustrated by the pictures.

Being fair

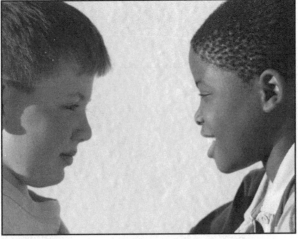

Smiling at someone

Helping someone carry there stuff

A boy is taking care of a animal

Removing something

Activity 2 - Think About It

According to Rasulullah ﷺ, "every joint of the body must perform a daily charity."

Look at the picture and write the "act of charity" next to the part of body it can do.

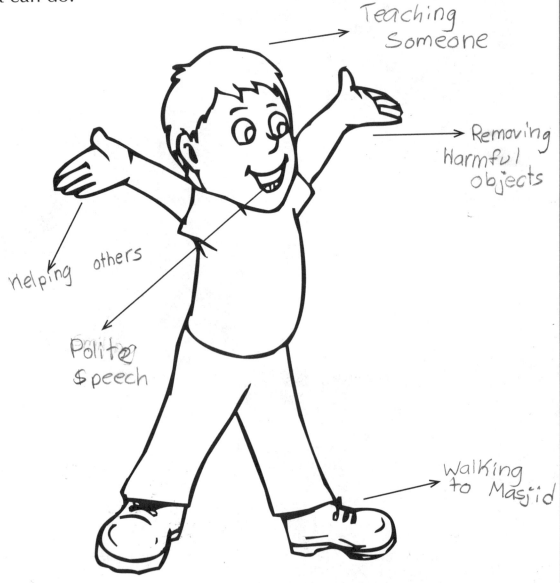

Teaching Someone

Removing harmful objects

helping others

Polite speech

Walking to Masjid

Polite speech, Walking to Masjid, Helping others, Removing harmful objects, Teaching someone

Activity 3

Read the clues from the sentences below. Write the missing word in the blank lines.

Hint: The numbers of spaces represent the number of letters in each word!

A. _S_ _a_ _d_ _a_ _q_ _a_ _h_ is an Arabic word for charity.

B. Helping some one _c_ _a_ _r_ _r_ _y_ his bags is also charity.

C. When we share with fellow _N_ _e_ _e_ _d_ _y_ _p_ _e_ _a_ _p_ _l_ _e_ . we are giving Sadaqah.

D. Being _n_ _i_ _c_ _e_ in treating others is a _c_ _h_ _a_ _r_ _i_ _t_ _y_ .

15

MAKING THE HAJJ

Activity 1: Comprehension

Look at the "concept map" below and write some important facts about Hajj in each section of the wheel.

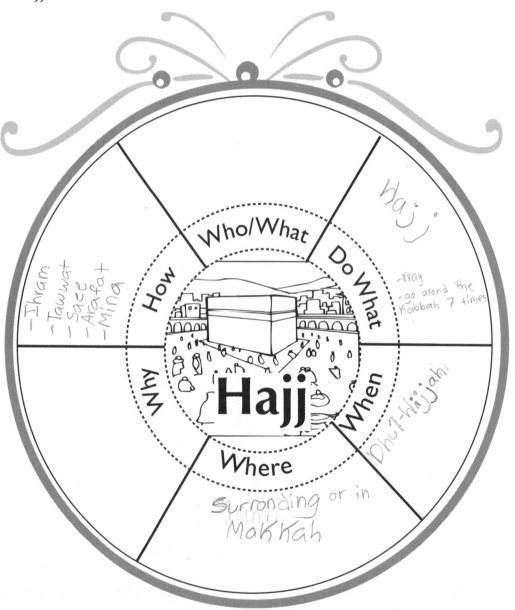

Wheel sections with handwritten notes:

- **Who/What**
- **Do What**: Hajj — Pray, go around the Kabbah 7 times
- **How**: Ihram, Tawwaf, Saee, Arafat, Mina
- **When**: Dhul-Hijjah
- **Where**: Surronding or in Makkah
- **Why**

Center: **Hajj**

Activity 2 - Think About It

A **simile** is a figure of speech in which two things are compared. Usually, it is found in a phrase introduced by the words "like" or "as".

A. Read the Hadith on page 58 of your textbook. Write the simile used to explain the benefits of Hajj.

_____

_____

_____

_____

B. Be creative and complete the similes below.

- Sweet as _____.

- Shiny as _____.

- Hard as _____.

- Soft as _____.

- Tall as _____.

Activity 3 - Show What You Know

Use the chart below to identify the parts of the story of Hajar ﷺ and Ismail ﷺ. Then write a summary of the story with your own title.

Title: _____

Author: _____

Setting

Where: _____

When: _____

Characters

Main Characters: _____

Other Characters: _____

Main Problem

_____

_____

_____

_____

_____

Solution to the Main Problem

_____
_____
_____
_____
_____

Story

_____
_____
_____
_____
_____
_____
_____
_____
_____
_____
_____
_____
_____
_____

16

GOOD MANNERS

Activity 1: Comprehension

Color the following pictures then write the good manner it represents.

Ihsan

Adl

Wikmah

Rahman
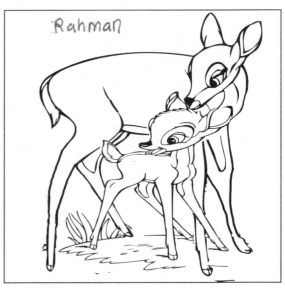

Words: **Ihsan**   **Rahmah**   **Adl**   **Hikmah**

Activity 2 - Think About It

Look below at the path from dawn to sunset. Write a deed at each number (part of the day) that shows the Adab and Akhlaq we must display in order to follow the teachings of Prophet Muhammad ﷺ.

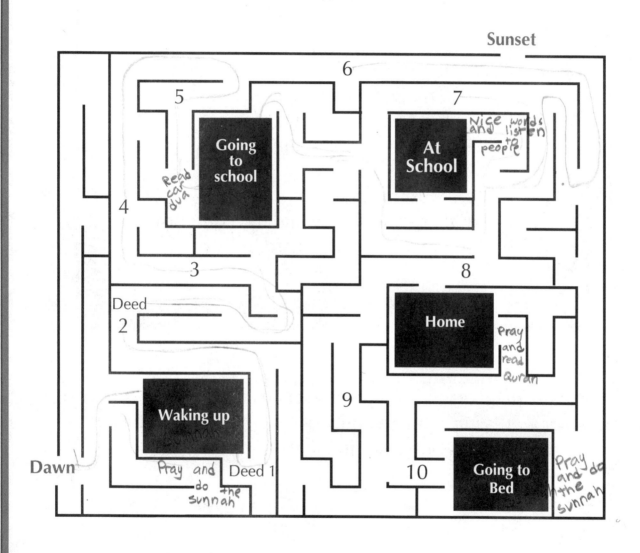

Activity 3 - Show What You Know

Read the poem below.

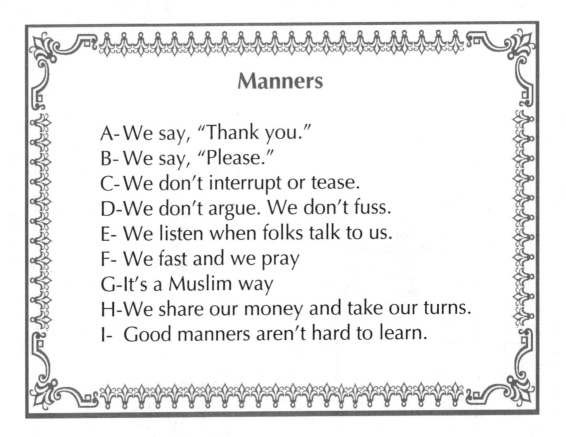

Manners

A- We say, "Thank you."
B- We say, "Please."
C- We don't interrupt or tease.
D- We don't argue. We don't fuss.
E- We listen when folks talk to us.
F- We fast and we pray
G- It's a Muslim way
H- We share our money and take our turns.
I- Good manners aren't hard to learn.

Sort out the manners that the poem teaches us. Pick out the most important words in each line and write it on the dashes below. Each dash represents one letter in the word.

A. T h a n k y o u

B. p l e a s e

C. t e a s e   (No)

D. f u s s   (No)

E. <u>Listen</u>

F. <u>fast</u> & <u>pray</u>

G. <u>way</u>

H. <u>Share</u>

I. <u>Good manners</u>

Activity 4 - Vocabulary

Use the following words and and complete each sentence.

A. We should follow Islamic _____ of behavior.

B. Rasulullah ﷺ advised his Sahabah ﷺ to make things
_____ for people.

C. Islam is a religion of _____ .

D. Allah ﷻ does not want us to face _____
when practicing our _____ .

WORDS:

code,   easy,   moderation,   hardship,   religion

17

THE CONCEPT OF HAYA'

Activity 1: Comprehension

Haya' is an important quality of a Muslim. In the concept map below write the actions that show Haya' in the four following categories.

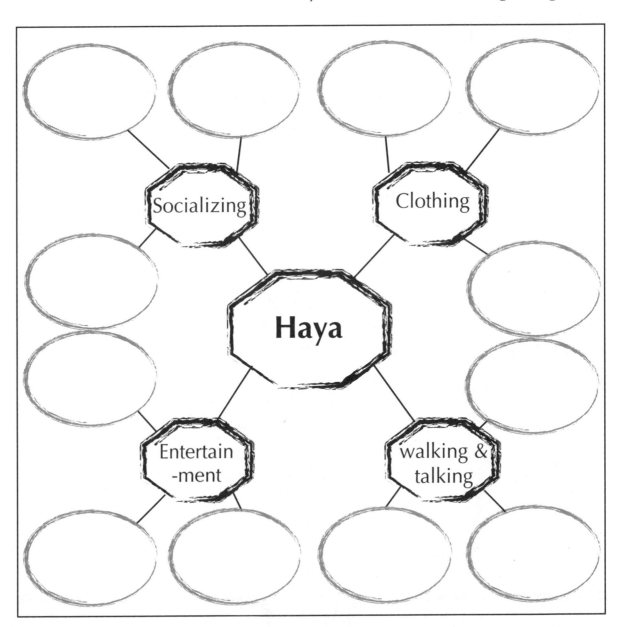

Activity 2 - Think About It

MODESTY AT HOME

Circle the situation in each of the following scenarios which shows modesty.

Situation 1

- Walking around the living room while changing into your school uniform.

- Changing in the privacy of your bedroom or bathroom.

Situation 2

- Allowing your friends to laugh loudly and use bad language while your parents are resting.

- Telling your friends to use polite language and speak softly because your parents are sleeping.

Scenario 3

- Turning off the TV whenever there is an improper scene or when the actors are using bad language.

- Watching TV and laughing when bad words are used in a show.

Activity 3 - Vocabulary

Complete following word puzzle.

Across	**Top to bottom**
1. People who wander from place to place	2. opposite of 'excess'
3. Travel to a holy place like Makkah	4. The English word for Haya'
5. Factories and cars pollute the _____.	6. Some one who obeys others
7. To give courage to someone	8. We should follow the ------- of Satr in our dress.

Words to Use

pilgrimage   obedient   nomads   code   moderation
modesty   encourage   environment

18

CONTROLLING ANGER

Activity 1: Comprehension

A. Islam is a religion of peace and love. Draw a small poster below to show the peaceful nature of Islam.

Islam

B. Why do you think Rasulullalh ﷺ kept repeating his advice to the man when he said, "control your anger"?

_____

_____

_____

_____

_____

_____

_____

C. Write down one example from the life of Rasulullah ﷺ when he controlled his anger, even when he was hurt and bullied by the Kuffar.

_____

_____

_____

_____

_____

_____

_____

_____

Activity 2 - Think About It!

Read the first paragraph on page 72 of your textbook and complete the following 'concept map' about Ahmad, who is a Muttaqi.

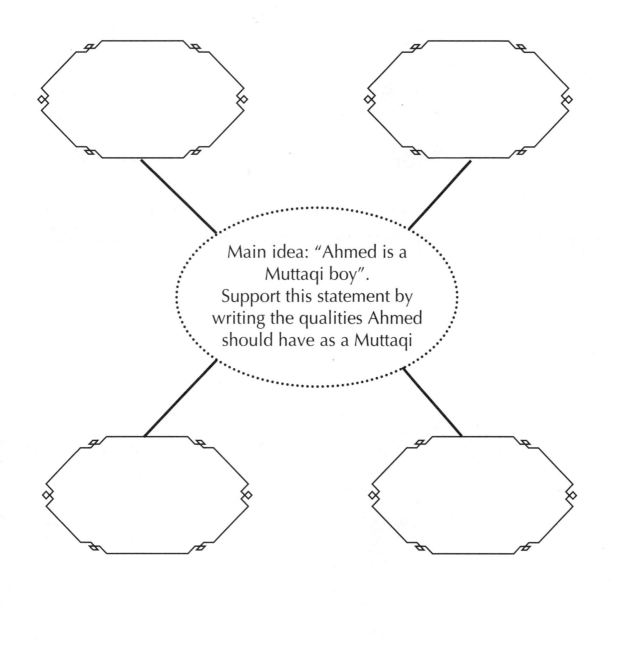

Main idea: "Ahmed is a Muttaqi boy".
Support this statement by writing the qualities Ahmed should have as a Muttaqi

Activity 3 - Show What You Know

Read the Ayah below.

ٱلَّذِينَ يُنفِقُونَ فِى ٱلسَّرَّآءِ وَٱلضَّرَّآءِ وَٱلْكَـٰظِمِينَ ٱلْغَيْظَ وَٱلْعَافِينَ عَنِ ٱلنَّاسِ ۗ وَٱللَّهُ يُحِبُّ ٱلْمُحْسِنِينَ ﴿١٣٤﴾

Those who spend (in Allah's cause) in ease and in difficulty; those who control their anger and are forgiving towards mankind.
Allah loves the doers of good.
(Surah al-Imran:3:134)

According to the above Ayah which actions are liked by Allah ﷻ?

A. _____

B. _____

C. _____

70

19

BEING ACCOUNTABLE

Activity 1: Comprehension

Explain the concept of "accountability" in Islam in your own words.

_____

_____

Activity 2 - Think About It!

Draw a line to match each person with his or her responsibility.

Person	Is Responsible For
Worker	The safety and well-being of citizens
Imam	Educating of students
President	To be on time and work hard
Teacher	teaching and leading people in prayer
Citizenszens	To obey the laws of the country

Write sentences about the things you are accountable for towards Allah ﷻ, at home, and in the classroom.

Allah ﷻ: _____

At Home: _____

In the Classroom: _____

Activity 3

Read Ayah 85 of Surah an-Nisa and list some "good causes" you would like to join.

_____   _____

_____   _____

_____   _____

_____   _____

_____   _____

_____   _____

_____   _____

20

THE QUR'AN AND HADITH

Activity 1: Comprehension

"Good people are people we can trust. They are honest; they tell the truth. They keep promises; if they say they will do something, they do it. They are loyal. Good people always do the right thing, even if saying or doing the right thing gets them into trouble."

Read following "Dos and Don'ts" of being honest, keeping your promises and being loyal to Allah  and His Prophet . Sort out the statements in the table of Dos and Don'ts.

- Tell only the truth.
- Say what you mean.
- Use bad words when you're mad.
- Keep your promises.
- Say that you will do something without really doing it.
- Tell lies.
- If you find something return it to its owner.
- Steal.
- Cheat.
- Return the things you borrow.
- Only say you will do the things you think you really can do.
- Bully smaller classmates.
- Be fair.
- Make promises you can't keep.

Do	Don't
Tell only the truth	Use Bad words when your mad
Say what you mean	Say that you will do something without really doing it
keep your promises	Tell lies
If you find something return it to it's owner.	steal
	cheat

74

Activity 2 - Think About It

Write a story about how you kept a promise you made to someone. Use the guidelines below to make notes. This will help you organize your story.

Title: _____

Author: _____

Settings

_____

_____

_____

_____

_____

Characters

Main Characters: _____

Other Characters: _____

The story

Conclusion
(The Ending)

_____

_____

_____

_____

_____

_____

_____

_____

_____

_____

_____

_____

_____

_____

Activity 3 - Use What You Know

Did you read the story about Abdul Qadir al-Jilani? Let's follow his example for the next two weeks and always keep our promises no matter what.

Design the Covers:

Make a "My Promise Coupon" book.
Make a front and a back cover.
Make any design on a piece of 4x3 construction paper.
Write "My Promise Coupon Book" on the cover.

Make the coupons:

Cut the construction paper the same size as your cover (4x3)
Design a border for the coupons
Copy the form below into your coupon page

I, _____

Promise to: _____

Signature: _____

Make two or three coupons. Then staple the book together. You can make a promise to someone or to yourself. Just remember to keep the promise!

21

BEING PERSISTENT AND CONSISTENT

Activity 1: Comprehension

Read the following stories and write a 'P" in front of those which show persistence and a "C" in front of those which show consistency.

_C_ 1. A spider is trying to spin a web. The web keeps breaking. The spider spins the web again and again until it is complete.

_C_ 2. Dilshad is learning to knit. Every time she drops a loop, she has to go back and start all over again.

_P_ 3. The turtle won the race because he did not stop, even when he was way behind.

_P_ 4. The hare lost the race because he stopped when he thought he was ahead.

_C_ 5. Idris makes sure he reads a little part of the Qur'an every day.

Activity 2 - Think About It!

Remember the quality mentioned in Lesson 21. List three ways you do something consistently for each of the categories below.

1. Things you do with consistency at home:

1. Draw

2. Brush teeth

2. Things you do with consistency at school:

1. Do work

2. Pray salah

3. Things you do with consistency to stay clean:

1. do wudu

2. Take a shower

4. Things you do with consistency to obey Allah ﷻ:

1. Pray

2. Make dua

Activity 3 - Vocabulary

Vocabulary Review Lessons 18 - 21

Circle the words below in the puzzle.

```
N  N  O  P  E  R  S  R  O  C  N  E  L  S  H  A  L  S
L  U  H  A  V  E  E  A  A  B  N  U  U  R  D  E  N  R
L  A  D  I  D  V  O  R  N  V  H  L  F  I  M  G  R  E
E  A  T  I  E  E  A  R  I  T  H  I  G  A  N  H  E  K
C  A  N  N  H  V  B  R  E  T  E  O  N  A  R  E  H  A
T  A  G  K  A  S  O  G  E  B  E  N  I  R  Z  C  Z  T
R  E  K  N  X  N  A  R  W  K  J  O  N  B  R  U  S  E
O  E  N  U  M  R  C  R  Y  R  J  F  A  U  W  F  X  R
H  F  A  E  U  E  S  J  R  R  W  A  E  T  E  V  S  A
L  D  N  O  S  H  A  B  W  A  T  L  M  J  L  I  I  C
S  T  C  M  O  D  E  S  T  Y  H  L  M  Q  F  Q  E  H
D  N  O  H  H  B  E  R  V  L  R  A  N  F  A  L  I  W
E  U  K  Q  N  D  A  P  Q  D  U  H  F  O  R  M  R  A
K  P  O  B  M  V  Q  N  O  B  D  W  A  A  E  P  B  V
X  U  C  W  P  N  S  C  D  Z  I  W  B  W  L  S  Z  G
A  C  C  O  U  N  T  A  B  I  L  I  T  Y  A  U  J  T
C  I  U  K  J  D  E  L  G  U  T  H  C  M  S  A  H  Q
Y  L  V  K  B  A  R  M  E  Q  Z  K  J  O  Z  D  F  K
```

ACCOUNTABILITY	ENVIRONMENT
BANDIT	MODESTY
CARAVAN	REVENGE
CARETAKERS	SECRET
CRUEL	TAWBAH
	WELFARE

22

BEING A GOOD NEIGHBOR

Activity 1: Comprehension

Match each of the neighborly duties listed below to the correct picture.

RESPECT   CARE HELPING   WORKING TOGETHER

Activity 2 - Think About It

There are other types of neighbors besides the people who live next to you. Often these neighbors are people from your community that you see all the time. Write how you can do an act of kindness for each type of the neighbor below.

A. A person sitting next to you on the bus or train:

Help them with something

B. The children in your classroom:

Say salam

C. Your mailman:

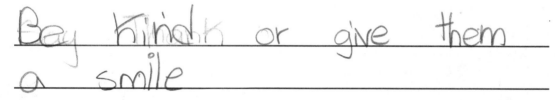

Bay kind or give them a smile

D. Your garbage collector:

Say Jazakullah or Thank you

Activity 3 - Use What You Know

Read Ayah 36 of Surah an-Nisa'. Then write a sentence about how you could serve each of the people below.

People	How I can serve them
Parents	Wash the dishes for them
Relatives	Invite them to your house
Orphans	give food or money
Needy	give clothes or money
Neighbors	give gifts or help them carry groceries.
Travelers	say welcome to our country or greet them

HELPING OTHERS

Activity 1: Comprehension

Read the following statements and select the correct answer.

A.

> "Don't worry! Allah would never abandon you! You care for your relatives, you help others, you provide for the poor, you show hospitality to the guest, and you are just and kind."
>
> Who said these words to Rasulullah ﷺ?
>
> ◯ Khadijah ◯ Abu Bakr
>
> ◯ Fatimah ◯ 'Umar

B. Use the quote you just read and color the shapes which tell us about Rasulullah's loving character.

Activity 2- Show What You Know

This week show kindness to others by doing as many of the activities below that as can. Keep a journal for one week. For each day make one entry in your journal explaining which act of kindness you did. Share your journal entries with the class the following week.

Learn patience and gain peace

- Do not criticize or say anything bad about anyone this week. Pay attention and listen to others. Show kindness every time you can.

_____

Show kindness

- Share some treats from your lunch box during lunch. Invite someone who is being bullied to sit next to you at lunch time.

_____

Be helpful when taking a bus ride

- Make room for another student next to you on the school bus. Give a thank you note to your bus driver.

_____

Keep Warm

- Collect unused clothes from around your house. Include old coats. Donate these clothes to a local homeless shelter.

_____

Activity 3 - Think About It

Read Ayah 2 of Surah al-Ma'idah and color the pictures that show "Righteousness and Piety." Cross out the pictures that show "Aggression."

24

HONORING OUR PARENTS

Activity 1: Comprehension

What does Rasulullah (S) want us to do when he says, "honor your parents"?

He wants us to be good to our parents.

Write some of the ways you honor your dear parents in the graphic organizer below.

Help them do chores

Let them rest

Say Nice words to them

Shovel the snow for them

WAYS I HONOR MY PARENTS:

Give them gifts

Help them cook

HAPPY ME

Activity 2 - Think About It

Write an "acrostic" poem using the letters in the topic word "parents".

In an acrostic poem first you pick a word. Then place the letters of that word vertically (up and down) on your paper. Next think of a word, phrase, or sentence that starts with each letter to describe your subject.

EXAMPLE:

Sun shines brightly
Up in the sky
Nice and warm on my skin.

(This poem is about the sun. It uses the letters in the word sun.)

Now, you write an acrostic using the letters in the topic word "Parents".

(P) _____

(A) _____

(R) _____

(E) _____

(N) _____

(T) _____

(S) _____

Activity 3- Your Heredity

We think, look and act like our parents and grandparents. The traits we get from our parents and grand parents make up our "heredity." Think about your heredity by finding out about traits you share with your parents.

You

Height _____
Color of hair _____
Type of hair
Color of eyes _____
Tone of skin _____

Your Mother

Height _____
Color of hair _____
Type of hair _____
(Curly, straight etc.)
Color of eyes _____
Color of skin _____

Your Father

Height _____
Color of hair _____
Type of hair _____
(Curly, straight etc.)
Color of eyes _____
Color of skin _____

Complete the following form

1. My hair is like my _____ .

2. My eye color is like my _____ .

3. My hair type is like my _____ .

4. My skin color is like my _____ .

5. Think of some other characteristics you got from your mother or father (such as the shape of your nose, chin, your personality or special talents).

My Ancestors

Write a paragraph explaining what you know about your ancestors.

_____

_____

_____

_____

_____

_____

_____

_____

_____

25

LOVE, CARE AND MERCY

Activity 1: Comprehension

A. Two of the most repeated names of Allah ﷻ are "The Compassionate" and "The Merciful". Write the Arabic words for these two holy Names of Allah ﷻ.

The Compassionate: _____

The Merciful: _____

B. Whom did Allah ﷻ send as the greatest symbol of His Mercy?

_____

_____

C. Why is it important for us to live in peace with other people?

_____

_____

D. What can happen if we have negative feelings towards other people?

_____

_____

Activity 2 - Think About It

Think of a motto that encourages Muslims to love, have mercy, and take care of one another. Design a t-shirt that shows the motto and artwork to go with it.

Motto: _____

Activity 3 - Vocabulary

Complete the following crossword puzzle

Across	Up and down
1. Act of being thankful	2. To come together
3. Opposite of positive	4. Envy, feeling of being jealous
5. Release, get rid of	6. Act of forgiving
7. Sympathy, kindness	8. We ---- not hate our parents.

Words: United, compassion, Jealousy, relieve, forgiveness, negative, thankfulness, love

26

FRIENDSHIP

Activity 1: Comprehension

Read the qualities of the following individuals. Choose the individuals that you would like to be your friends. Give reasons for your choices.

A. Ali's parents love him very much. He always obeys them and listens to their advice carefully.

B. Selma likes to read new books. She volunteers at a home for senior citizens. She takes new books from the library for the people living in the home.

C. Edin loves to play basketball. He is a very good player. Often, he misses his Fard prayers because he does not want to leave in the middle of the game.

D. Yasmina and her two friends always bully other girls in the class, so everyone is scared of Yasmina and her friends.

E. Ahmad and Parvez are good friends. They study very hard and score A's in every test. They treat every one in the class with respect and care. They are always ready to help everyone.

Reasons for your choices:

_____

_____

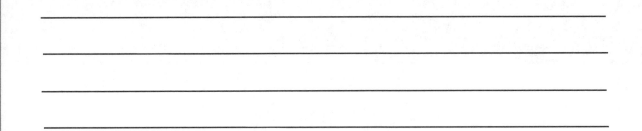

Activity 2 - Think About It

FRIENDSHIP GARDEN

Color the friendship garden below with bright colors. In the middle of each flower write one thing you will do to take care of your friend

Activity 3 - Use What You Know

Read the story of the two friends Pythias and Damon in the Hadith in Action section of this lesson.

Think of a friend of Rasulullah ﷺ who put his life in danger to protect Rasulullah ﷺ from harm. Write the story in your own words below:

_____

_____

_____

_____

_____

_____

_____

_____

_____

_____

_____

_____

_____

_____

27

COOPERATION AND UNITY

Activity 1: Comprehension

Think about the ways Rasulullah ﷺ brought Arab tribes together to live in peace. Read the following events from the life of Rasulullah ﷺ. How did unity help Rasulullah ﷺ and the Muslims achieve their goal in each event?

The Tribes of 'Aws and Khazraj in Madinah after the migration of the Muslims to Madinah

_____

_____

_____

The Muslims in the Battle of Badr

_____

_____

_____

The Muslims in the Battle of the Ditch

_____

_____

_____

Activity 2 - Think about it

A "parable" is a story which illustrates a moral or religious lesson. A parable is different from a fable. A fable uses animals, plants, objects and forces of nature as characters. A parable uses human characters. The Prophet ﷺ used a parable in this Hadith to emphasize the importance of unity for a strong and successful community.

Read the Hadith and write the parable used by Rasulullah ﷺ.

_____

_____

Now read the Hadith in each of the following lessons of this textbook and write the fable or parable used.

A. Lesson 12 (Praying on Time)

The parable or fable used in this Hadith is:

_____

_____

B. Lesson 27 (Cooperation and Unity)

The parable or fable used in the "looking ahead" section of this lesson is

_____

_____

Activity 3- Qur'an Connection

Read Ayah 2 of Surah Al-Ma'idah and write about a time you cooperated with someone to do a good action. Then write about a time you decided not to cooperate with someone to do a 'wrong action.'

**My story of cooperation
in doing a good action.**

_____

_____

_____

_____

_____

_____

**My story of not
cooperating in doing a wrong action**

_____

_____

_____

_____

_____

_____

28

HALAL AND HARAM

Activity 1: Comprehension - Name the three

A. Animals whose meat is Halal _____, _____, _____.

B. Pieces of an outfit which Muslim girls can wear
_____ ___,_____,_____.

C. Beverages (drinks) which are Haram
_____,_____,_____.

Activity 2 : Answer the following questions in complete sentences.

1. What are the rules related to Halal and Haram called?

    _____

2. Who has given us the laws of Halal and Haram?

    _____

3. What are the "doubtful matters"?

    _____

4. What are the scholars of Fiqh called?

    _____

Activity 3 - Use What You Know

Analogy Match: Choose the answer that best matches the analogy.

Help is to hinder,
As:
1. Aid is to assist
2. Below is to underneath
3. inside is to outside
4. fall is to injury

Fiqh is to Fuqhah,
As:
1. 'Ilm is to 'Ulama
2. Medicine is to a doctor
3. steal is to a thief
4. truth is to a liar

Tripod is to three
As:
1. Bin is to trash
2. Trick is to deceive
3. binary is to two
4. base is to bin

Halal is to permitted
As:
1. Read is to write
2. Haram is to prohibited
3. mother is to father
4. old is to young

Moderation is to excess
As:
1. Small is to large
2. Eat is to drink
3. strong is to powerful
4. good is to better

29

RIGHTEOUS AND HEALTHY LIVING

Activity 1: Comprehension

Write the correct answer in the blank space.

A. Muslims should always earn their living in a _____ way.

Proper   Halal   Haram

B. We should also _____ our money with the poor and needy.

earn   save   share

C. The powerful tyrant who fought with Prophet Dawud ﷺ was _____ .

Jalut   Ravanna   Loki

D. Prophet Dawud ﷺ received Allah's Book, the _____.

Tawrat   Zabur   Injil

Activity 2 - Think About It

Which activities do you think will help us live a righteous life? Complete the graphic organizer.

Righteous Influences: (books, TV programs, friends, community, and family)

Righteous Thoughts: whatever you think and believe makes you act in a certain way.

Righteous Actions: actions make you the kind of person you are.

Righteous Influences

Righteous Thoughts

Righteous Me

Righteous Words

Righteous Actions

Activity 3 - Writing Similes

Complete the following similes.

1. Large as a _____ .

2. Busy as a _____ .

3. Light as a _____ .

4. Small as a _____ .

5. Good as _____ .

Words

Bee, pea, mountain, feather, gold

EATING AND DRINKING IN MODERATION

Activity 1: Comprehension

Write a paragraph that explains, in your own words, the guidance of Rasulullah  about eating and drinking. Be sure to include a topic sentence, at least three details, and a closing sentence.

_____

_____

_____

_____

_____

_____

_____

_____

_____

_____

_____

_____

_____

Activity 2 - Think About It

A. Study the food pyramid below and make a healthy and balanced breakfast, lunch, and dinner menu. Use the guidance from Rasulullah ﷺ.

Breakfast Menu

Grain: ....

Fruit / Vegetable: ....

Dairy: ....

Meat: ....

Drink: ....

Lunch Menu

Grain: ....

Fruit / Vegetable: ....

Dairy: ....

Meat: ....

Drink: ....

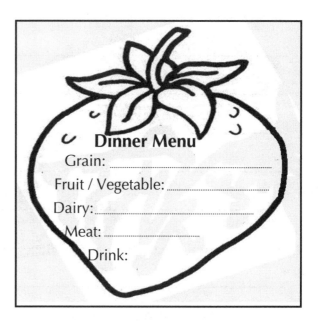

Dinner Menu

Grain: ....

Fruit / Vegetable: ....

Dairy: ....

Meat: ....

Drink:

B. Look at the following illustrations color and circle the ones you will include in your breakfast, lunch or dinner.

بِسْمِ اللهِ الرَّحْمٰنِ الرَّحِيمِ

اَللّٰهُمَّ صَلِّ عَلَى مُحَمَّدٍ

وَعَلَى اٰلِ مُحَمَّدٍ كَمَا صَلَّيْتَ

عَلَى اِبْرَاهِيْمَ وَعَلَى اٰلِ اِبْرَاهِيْمَ

اِنَّكَ حَمِيْدٌ مَجِيْدٌ

اَللّٰهُمَّ بَارِكْ عَلَى مُحَمَّدٍ وَّعَلَى

اٰلِ مُحَمَّدٍ كَمَا بَارَكْتَ عَلَى

اِبْرَاهِيْمَ وَعَلَى اٰلِ اِبْرَاهِيْمَ

اِنَّكَ حَمِيْدٌ مَجِيْدٌ